PUZZLES AND QUIZZLES

Puzzles and

illustrated by QUENTIN BLAKE

Quizzles

HELEN JILL FLETCHER

Abelard-Schuman London • New York

An Intext publisher

ALSO BY HELEN JILL FLETCHER:
Put on Your Thinking Cap

Third Impression, 1973

Copyright © 1971 by Helen Jill Fletcher
Library of Congress Catalogue Card Number: 78-132191
ISBN: 0 200 71760 x   Trade
         0 200 71771 5   Reinforced Edition
Printed in United States
Designed by The Etheredges

NEW YORK
Abelard-Schuman
Limited
257 Park Avenue So.
10010

LONDON
Abelard-Schuman
Limited
450 Edgware Road W2 1EG
and
24 Market Square Aylesbury

INTRODUCTION

Psychologists have found that young children have the ability to think and reason at a much younger age than was formerly believed possible. They have discovered that when a child is asked a problem question, he can very often come up with an answer that is both sensible and logical despite the fact that he had never heard an explanation of the problem before.

With this in mind, the author has provided a number of simple thought agitators for young children on a variety of subjects, all designed to stimulate interest and arouse an eagerness to think. For learning to think is the first step in learning to read well.

1. Here is an easy puzzle, to begin with:

Mother made a cheesecake
　　She made it in the round
Someone stole a piece of it
　　And never made a sound.
But no one ever ate the piece
　　So it can still be found
If someone really clever
　　Turns this picture

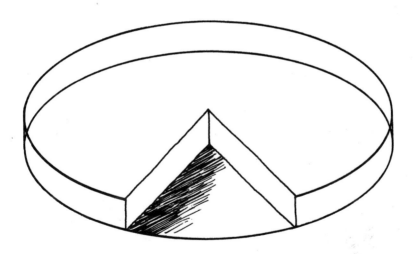

2. This one is not so easy!

Can you divide this circle into eight sections
by making just three lines?
The lines do not have to be straight.
The sections do not have to be of equal size.

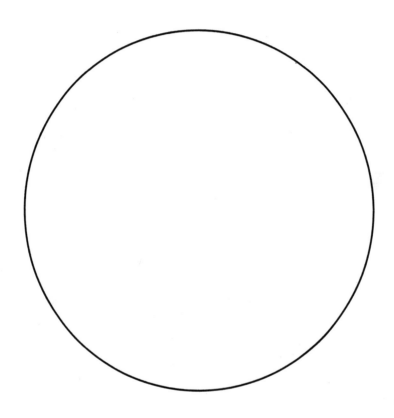

3. Can you answer these quizzles?

Which lays eggs?
Which gives milk?
Which gives honey?
Which wears a saddle?
Which swims in a pond?
Which sits by the fire?
Which lives in a jungle?

duck

tiger

bee

horse

hen

cow

cat

4. Look at the pictures in Column A.
Look at the pictures in Column B.

Find a picture in Column A that goes with a
picture in Column B.

Column A

Column B

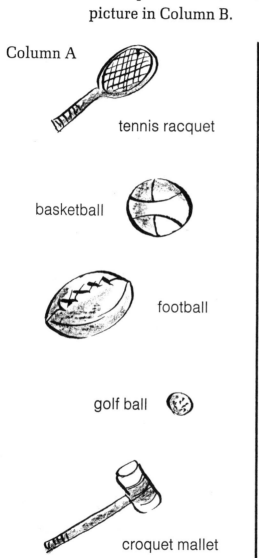

tennis racquet

basketball

football

golf ball

croquet mallet

5. Can you fill in this Thanksgiving Day menu?

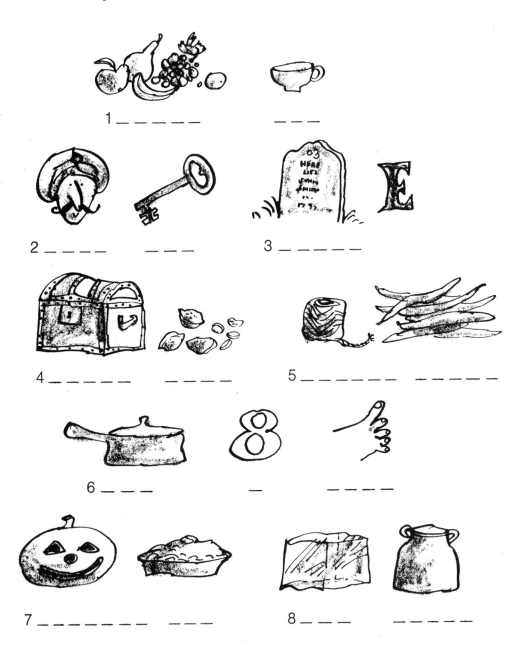

1 _ _ _ _ _   _ _ _

2 _ _ _ _   _ _ _ _

3 _ _ _ _ _ _

4 _ _ _ _ _   _ _ _ _

5 _ _ _ _ _ _ _   _ _ _ _ _

6 _ _ _   _   _ _ _ _

7 _ _ _ _ _ _ _ _   _ _ _

8 _ _ _ _   _ _ _ _ _

6. Which of the creatures in this quizzle
do you usually see with others of their kind?

Which do you usually see alone?

bird

squirrel

dog

duck

frog

rabbit

turtle

worm

chicken

7. Can you place these squares on the post
so that the largest square goes on first,
the next largest goes on second, and so on?

Now can you place them on the post,
starting with the smallest square on the bottom
and ending with the largest square on the top?

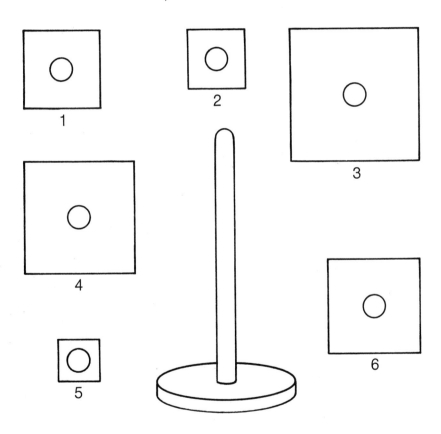

8. Which of these items can't you buy or sell?

apple

Big Dipper

clouds

tree

rain

watch

blocks

top

sun

9. Which of the objects shown here does the barber use when he cuts your hair?

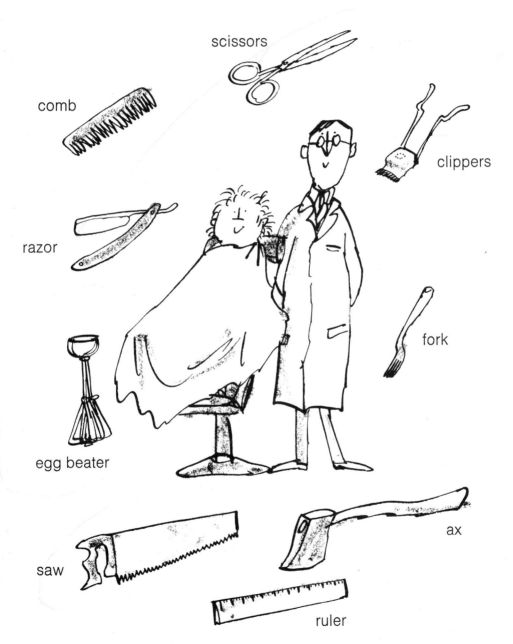

scissors

comb

clippers

razor

fork

egg beater

saw

ax

ruler

10. Can you figure out this puzzle?

Jeffrey needed a small square of wood (Figure A). But all he could find was a large piece of pegboard many times the size of the piece he needed (Figure B). How did Jeffrey get the piece he needed?

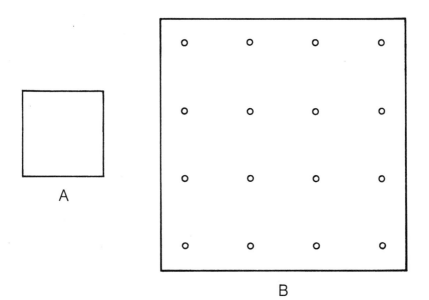

A

B

11. Can you pick out four figures in this quizzle that are alike in shape?

Can you pick out four other figures that are alike in shape?

Can you pick out four figures that are alike in some other way?

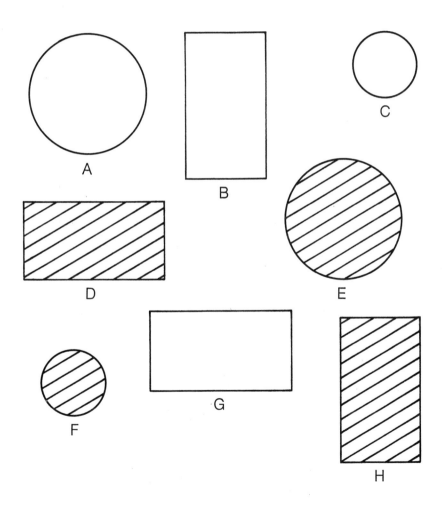

12. Can you draw a square half the size of this square
in one minute without lifting
your pencil off the paper?

13. Can you draw a square twice the size of this square
in one minute without lifting
your pencil off the paper?

14. In the Mean House at the zoo were twelve mean tigers
that were always fighting with each other.
Without changing the position of the tigers in the
following puzzle, can you divide the Mean House
into four sections of the same size
and shape, keeping three tigers in each section?

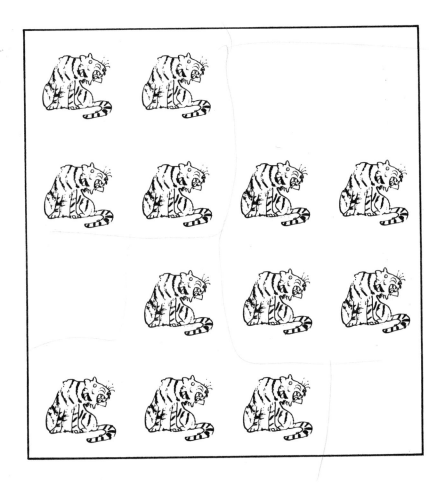

15. Arrange these seventeen buttons that have fallen out of the button barrel into four straight lines, with five buttons in each line.

16. Jamie had to go to school.
Jamie's mother had to go to the store.
Jamie's father had to go to the office.
Can you trace their separate paths without having
one path cross another and without
having any path go outside the square border?

17. Can you explain how each of the articles
shown here is used to hold or fasten things together?

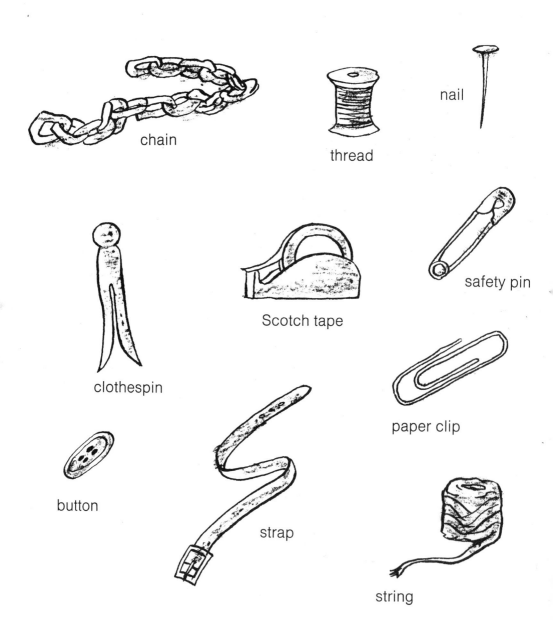

chain

thread

nail

clothespin

Scotch tape

safety pin

button

strap

paper clip

string

18. Which of the items on this page can be picked up by a magnet?

Do you know why?

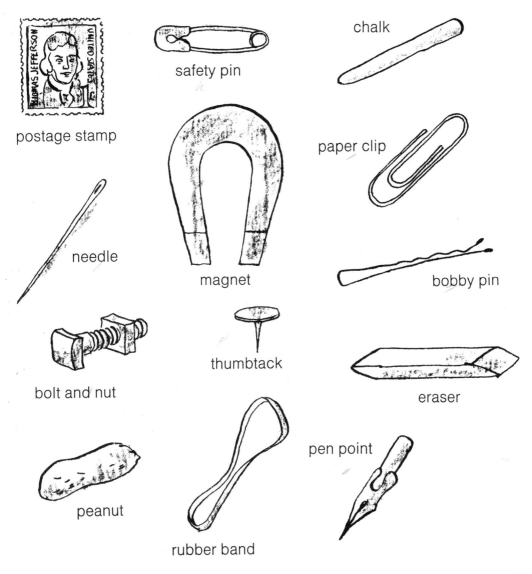

postage stamp

safety pin

chalk

needle

magnet

paper clip

bobby pin

bolt and nut

thumbtack

eraser

peanut

rubber band

pen point

19. The name of each of the three items in
Rows A, B and C rhymes with the names of the other
two items in that row. Can you give the rhyming words
in each row?

A	B	C

20. Can you answer this quizzle about weights and measures?

Which tells time?
Which measures inches?
Which measures milk or water or other liquids?
Which tells if you have a fever?
Which measures how heavy things are?

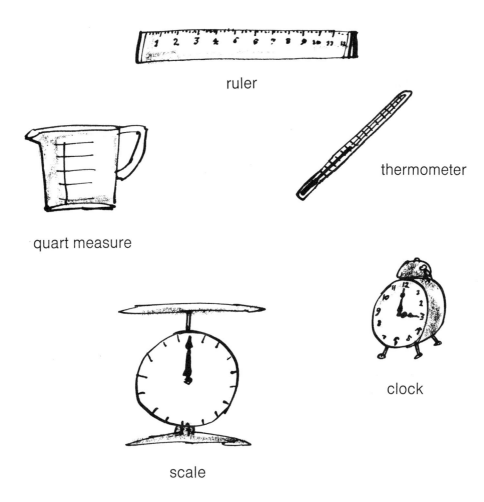

ruler

thermometer

quart measure

clock

scale

21. Which of the two items shown in each box is easier to pick up with your bare hands?

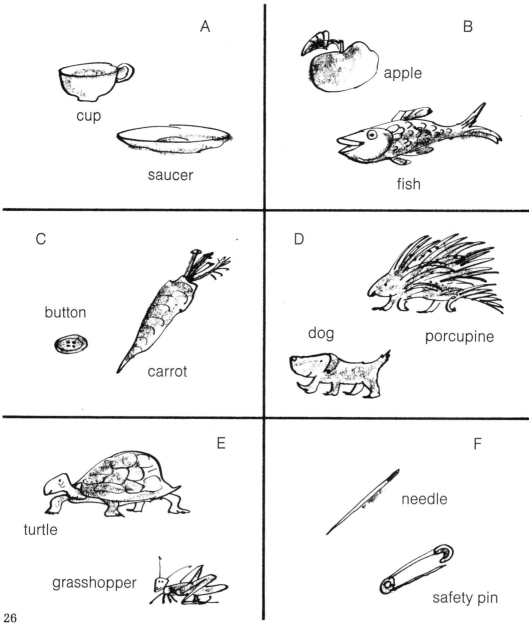

A

cup

saucer

B

apple

fish

C

button

carrot

D

dog

porcupine

E

turtle

grasshopper

F

needle

safety pin

22. Which of these creatures are jumpers?
Which are creepers?

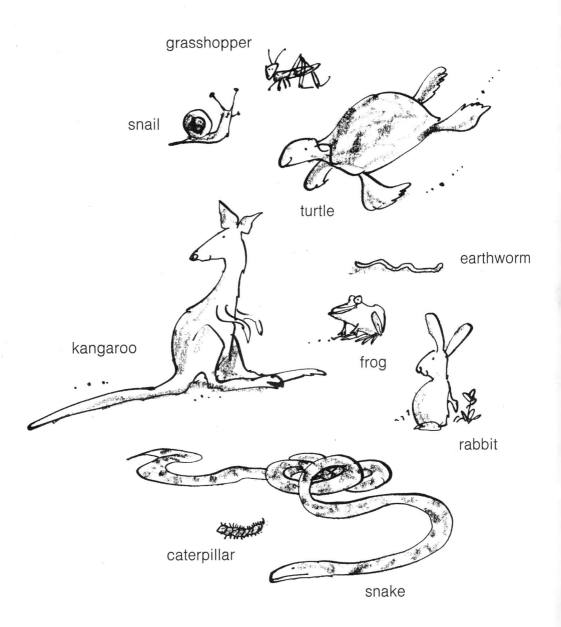

grasshopper

snail

turtle

kangaroo

earthworm

frog

rabbit

caterpillar

snake

23. In this puzzle:

Which has no legs?
Which has one leg?
Which has two legs?
Which has three legs?
Which has four legs?
Which has six legs?

horse

boy

stool

piano

stand

snowman

mouse

bird

dog

goose

ant

24. How many surfaces does each of the objects
in this quizzle have?

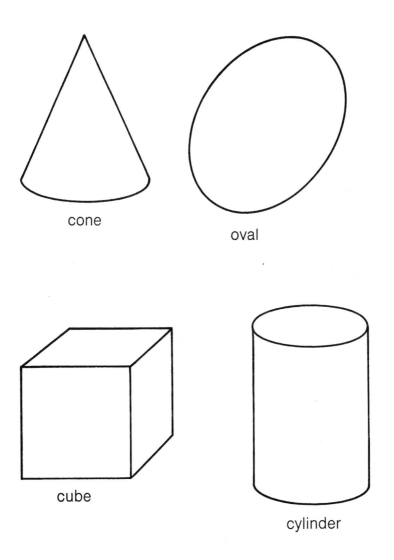

cone

oval

cube

cylinder

25. One day, Pamela went into the woods to paint a picture of a tree. There were five birds in the tree that looked alike. But one was different. Which one was different?

26. Can you tell which food each of
these animals eats?

cheese

bone

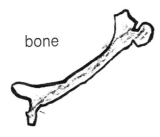

elephant

peanuts

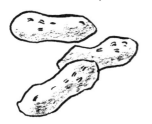

mouse

dog

27. Can you complete the rest of the sentence in the following quizzles?

Did you ever see

an egg _ _ _

a square _ _ _ _ _

a cat _ _ _ _ _

a horse _ _ _

28. Can you figure out this puzzle?

Bunny Rabbit decided to have some fun
one Easter Sunday, so this is the way he painted
the names on his Easter eggs.
Can you guess who the eggs are for?

29. Poor little Missy is lost in a big department store. Can you help her find the way out?

EXIT

30. How many ghosts can you find
in this haunted castle?

31. Which of these pictures makes you think of winter?

Which makes you think of summer?

Which makes you think of winter and summer?

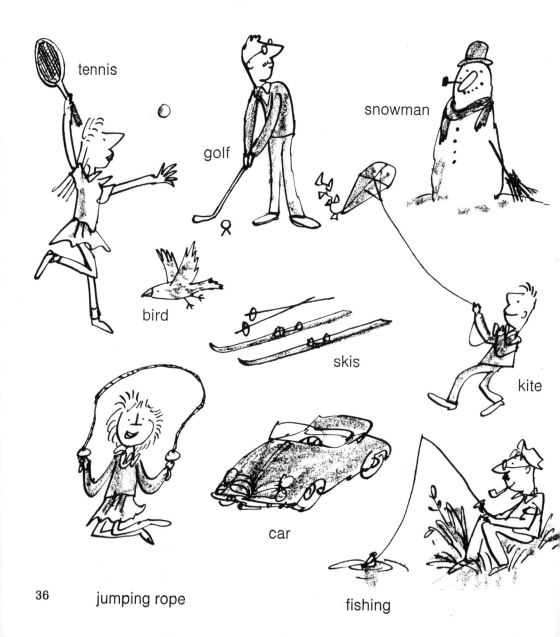

tennis

golf

snowman

bird

skis

kite

jumping rope

car

fishing

32. The shopkeeper who owns a certain grocery store
likes to play games with his customers.
This is the sign he put in his window.

Can you guess the names of some of the things
sold in his store?

A

B

C

D

E

F

33. There are four pictures each in rows A, B and C. One of the four pictures in each row does not belong with the other three pictures in that row.

Name the picture that does not belong.

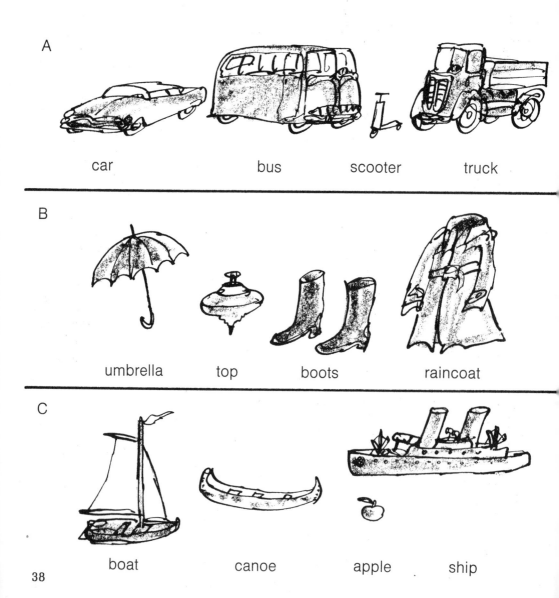

A

car   bus   scooter   truck

B

umbrella   top   boots   raincoat

C

boat   canoe   apple   ship

34. Which of these creatures carries his home with him on his back?

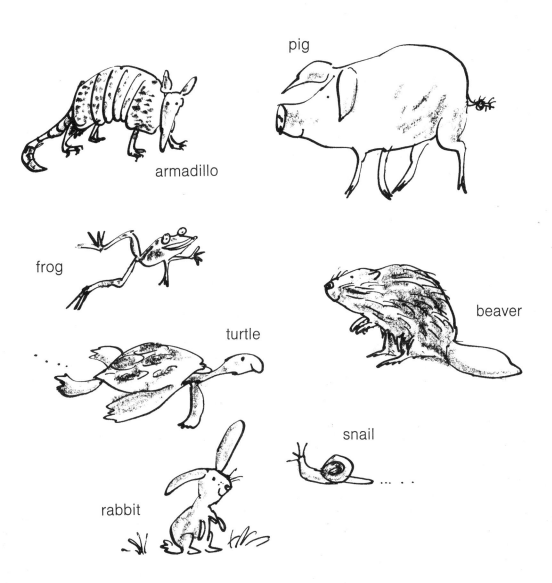

pig

armadillo

frog

turtle

beaver

snail

rabbit

35. What are each of these objects used for?

Can you show how each is used?

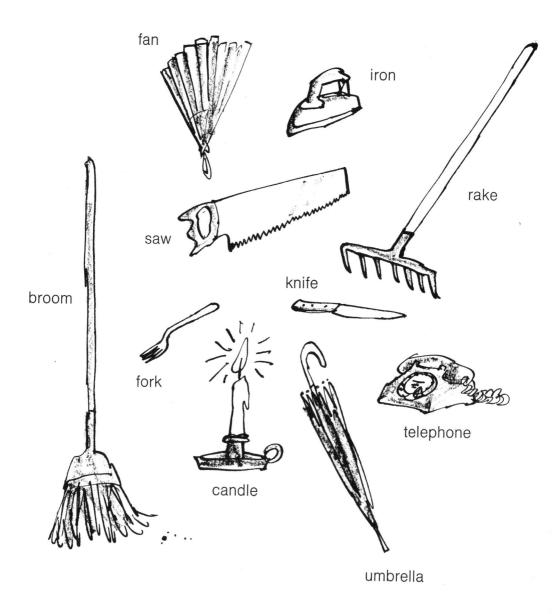

fan

iron

rake

saw

broom

knife

fork

candle

telephone

umbrella

36. Which of these articles is usually bought by the dozen?

Which is bought by the pound?
Which is bought by the bunch?
Which is bought by the head?
Which is bought one at a time?

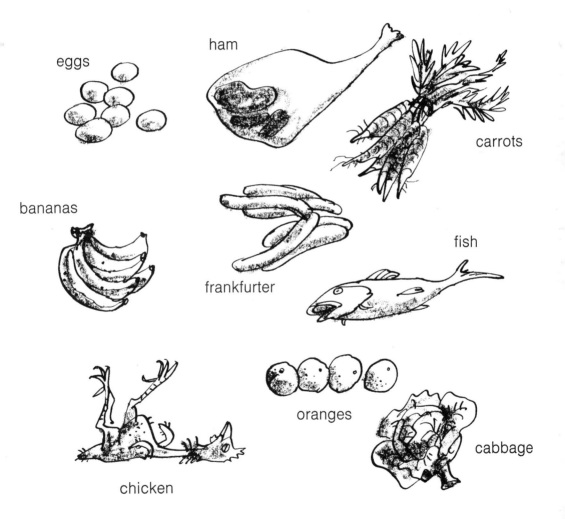

eggs

ham

carrots

bananas

frankfurter

fish

chicken

oranges

cabbage

37. Name each creature in this quizzle
and tell where it lives.

A  lives in a

A  lives in a

A  lives in a

A   lives in a

A   lives in a

A   lives in a

38. Three people are shown on this page,
each of whom is celebrating his birthday.

Can you tell which birthday cake is for which person?

A

B

C

Billy

Tom

Mary

39. Here are a number of articles usually found in a kitchen.

Which of the articles have covers?
Which of the articles do not have covers?

dish

casserole

syrup container

sugar bowl

measuring cup

cream pitcher

saucepan

salt and pepper shakers

40. Each picture-and-word combination below
is the name of a flower.

Can you name the flower?

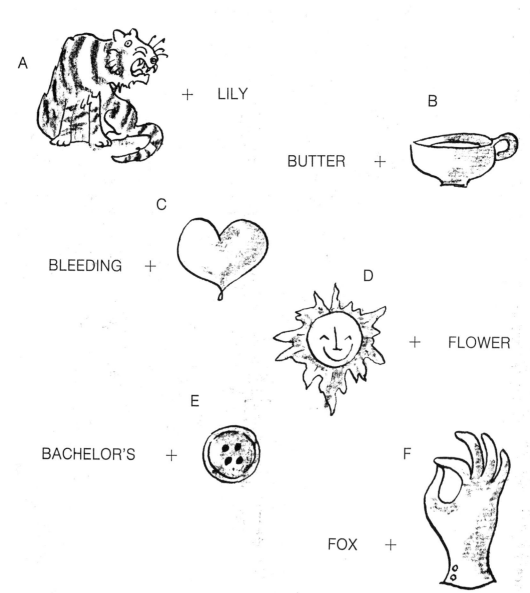

A   +   LILY

B

BUTTER   +

C

BLEEDING   +

D

+   FLOWER

E

BACHELOR'S   +

F

FOX   +

46

41. Each of the articles shown here is either hot or cold to the touch.

Which is hot?
Which is cold?

teakettle

candle

ice cream cone

electric light bulb

radiator

coffee

icicles

42. Find the shadow in this puzzle that belongs
  with each picture.

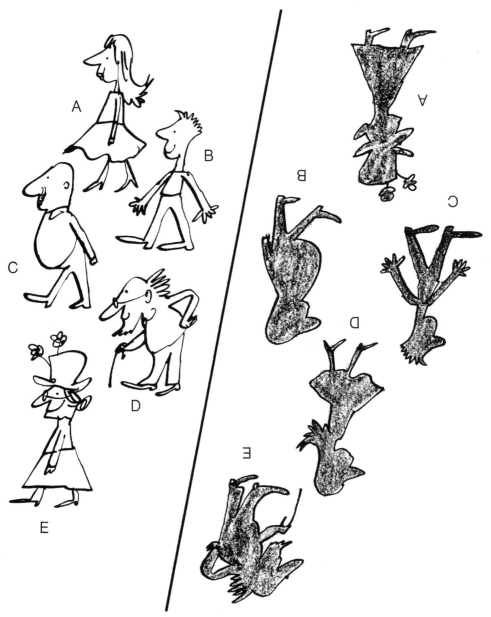

43. Which of these musical instruments make sounds

by being blown?
by being hit?
by being scraped or rubbed?

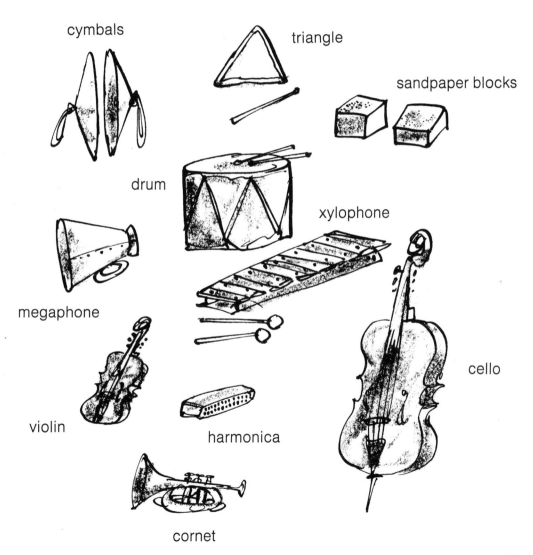

cymbals

triangle

sandpaper blocks

drum

xylophone

megaphone

violin

harmonica

cello

cornet

44. Which of these animals travel

by land?
by air?
by water?
underground?

earthworm

rabbit

bird

turtle

hen

dragonfly

mouse

snail

ant

frog

fish

45. In the Flea Market in Paris, they don't sell fleas
but they do sell almost everything else,
from expensive antique furniture to broken toys.
In the picture below, name the things you can find
that begin with the letter **b.**

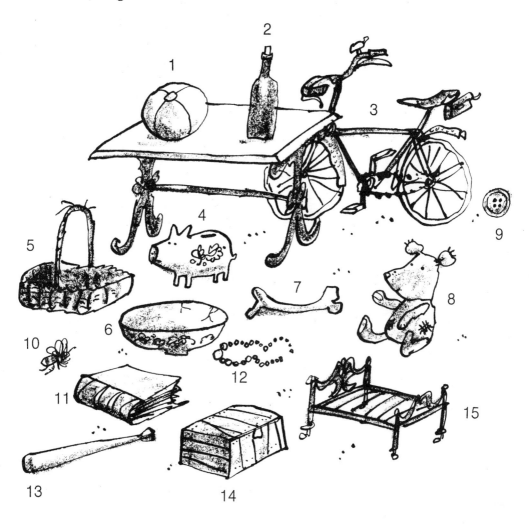

46. Can you solve this puzzle?

What do you have that each article shown here has, too?

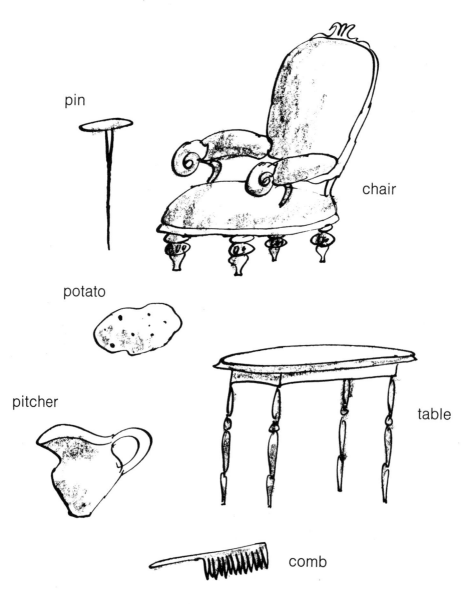

pin

chair

potato

pitcher

table

comb

ANSWERS

1. Upside down.   (last line)

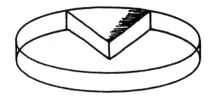

2.

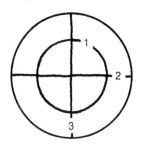

3. The hen and duck lay eggs.
   The cow gives milk.
   The bee gives honey.
   The horse wears a saddle.
   The duck swims in a pond.
   The cat sits by the fire.
   The tiger lives in a jungle.

4. The tennis racquet goes with the net.
   The basketball goes with the basket.
   The football goes with the goalposts.
   The golf ball goes with the bag.
   The croquet mallet goes with the wickets.

5. Thanksgiving Day menu

1 fruit cup   2 turkey   3 gravy
4 chestnuts   5 string beans   6 potatoes
7 pumpkin pie   8 ice cream

6. Usually found with others of their kind:

birds   ducks   chickens   squirrels

Usually found alone:

worms   rabbits   frogs   turtles   dogs

7. Squares on post, starting with largest:
3, 4, 6, 1, 2, 5

Squares on post, starting with smallest:
5, 2, 1, 6, 4, 3

8. You cannot buy or sell any of the following:

Big Dipper   clouds   rain   sun

9. The barber usually used the following:

scissors   comb   clippers

10.

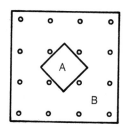

11. Four figures alike in shape:
A, C, E, F

Four other figures alike in shape:
B, D, G, H

Four figures alike in some other way:
D, E, F, H

12. A square half the size

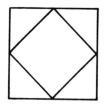

13. A square twice the size

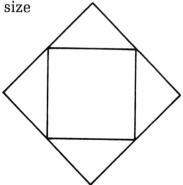

14. The Mean House divided into four sections of the same size:

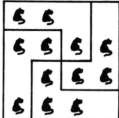

15. Seventeen buttons arranged in four straight lines with five buttons in each line:

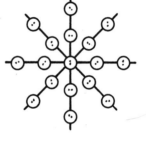

16. These are the paths that Jamie and his mother and father took:

17. A chain binds things together.
Thread is used to sew things together.
A nail is hammered into two pieces of wood.
A clothespin fastens clothes to a line.
Scotch tape sticks things together.
A safety pin pins things together.
A button closes coats or dresses.
A paper clip fastens papers together.
A strap binds things together.
String ties packages or things together.

18. Magnets pick up:

safety pins	needles	bobby pins	
thumbtacks	pen points	bolts and nuts	paper clips

(A magnet is a piece of steel or iron that attracts other metals.)

19. Words that rhyme are:

Row A — bed, sled, head
Row B — tree, key, bee
Row C — boat, coat, note

20. A clock tells time.
A ruler measures inches.
A quart measure measures milk or water or other liquids.
A thermometer tells if you have a fever.
Scales measure how heavy things are.

21. Objects easier to pick up are:

A. cup   B. apple   C. carrot
D. dog   E. turtle   F. safety pin

22. Jumpers are:
grasshoppers, frogs, kangaroos, rabbits

Creepers are:
snails, turtles, earthworms, snakes, caterpillars

23. The snowman has no legs.
The stand has one leg.
The bird, the boy and the goose have two legs.
The stool and the piano have three legs.
The horse, the mouse and the dog have four legs.
The ant has six legs.

24. The cone has two surfaces.
The oval has one surface.
The cube has six surfaces.
The cylinder has three surfaces.

25. Bird Number 3 is different.

26. The elephant eats peanuts.
The mouse eats cheese.
The dog eats the bone.

27. Did you ever see an egg box?
Did you ever see a square dance?
Did you ever see a catfish?
Did you ever see a horsefly?

28. The eggs are for:

1 Aunt Belle   2 Uncle Bill
3 Milton   4 Mother
5 Pansy   6 Aunt Rose
     7 Maybelle

29.

30. There are seven ghosts.

31. Winter pictures are:
snowman, skis

Summer pictures are:
tennis, golf, kite, bird, fishing, jumping rope

Winter and summer pictures are:
car, bird

32. Grocery store puzzle

A pineapple   B rice   C peas
D eggplant   E string beans   F pancake flour

33. A scooter   B top   C apple

34. Creatures that carry their homes with them:
turtle   snail   armadillo

35. The telephone is used to talk into.
The iron is used to press clothes.
The fan is used to cool yourself.
The rake is used to gather leaves.
The saw is used to cut logs.
The fork is used to pick up food.
The knife is used to cut food.
The broom is used to sweep things together.
The candle is used to light a dark place.
The umbrella is used to shield you from the rain.

36. Eggs, frankfurters and oranges are bought by the dozen.
Ham, chicken and cabbage are bought by the pound.
Carrots and bananas are bought by the bunch.
Cabbage is bought by the head.
Fish, frankfurter, oranges, ham, chicken, banana and
cabbage can be bought one at a time.

37. A bird lives in a cage.
A fish lives in a fish bowl.
A chicken lives in a coop.
A monkey lives in a tree.
A dog lives in a doghouse.
A cow lives in a barn.

38. Cake C is for Billy.
Cake B is for Tom.
Cake A is for Mary.

39. Articles with covers:
casserole, syrup container, sugar bowl,
salt and pepper shakers

Articles without covers:
dish, measuring cup, saucepan, cream pitcher

40. Flowers are:

A tiger lily   B buttercup
C bleeding heart   D sunflower
E bachelor's button   F foxglove

41. Hot to touch:
teakettle, candle, radiator, bulb, coffee

Cold to touch:
ice cream cone, icicles

42. Figures and shadows are:

Figure	Matching Shadow
A	D
B	C
C	B
D	E
E	A

43. By being blown:
megaphone, harmonica, cornet

By being hit:
cymbals, triangle, drum, xylophone

By being scraped or rubbed:
sandpaper blocks, violin, cello

44. By land:
earthworm, rabbit, turtle, hen, snail, ant, mouse, frog

By air:
bird, dragonfly

By water:
turtle, snail, fish, frog

Underground:
earthworm, ant

45.

1 ball	2 bottle	3 bicycle
4 bank	5 basket	6 bowl
7 bone	8 bear	9 button
10 bee	11 book	12 beads
13 bat	14 box	15 bed

46. A head (like a pin);
arms (like a chair);
eyes (like a potato);
legs (like a table);
a mouth (like a pitcher);
teeth (like a comb);